Ann found a friend. She discovered that a nice old gentleman lives on the top floor of her building, She calls him Nonno (Granddad in italian) but he isn't really her grandfather as she comes from America. She has been living in the centre of Rome near Piazza Venezia for a year and as her parents both work all day she is often alone at home. Now she spends her afternoons with Nonno and she is much happier. They went for a walk today and Nonno showed Ann an inscription on a house where Michelangelo used to live. After their walk they had tea at Nonno's house.

Nonno is a bibliophile, that is someone crazy about books. Every time she asks a question, he pulls out a book from his big library to show her a picture or explain something to her.

Well, Ann, how did school go today?

Fine.

Interesting, and what do you have to study for tomorrow?

I have to write something about Michelangelo and the Renaissance.

What big words these are; I say: do you know what the Renaissance is?

Yes, of course, the rebirth of culture and everything else. Nonno, I already know all about it, don't worry.

I'm not worried, but when a little girl like you tells me she knows everything I feel like laughing. It's not possible to know everything nowadays. In Michelangelo's time it was different; people knew much less and there were some brainy people who really knew almost everything. Michelangelo as a boy lived in the house of Lorenzo il Magnifico, who was the wealthiest and most important man in Florence. Every day Lorenzo invited artists, writers, philosophers and poets to dinner to discuss about all the beautiful and interesting things that were then being discovered. Come on, I'll show you some books about Michelangelo.

Nonno pulls out one book after another on Michelangelo: drawings, sculptures, the Sistine Chapel... he did so many things !

> I still have to show you a very special book I found many years ago in the attic of a house that was being demolished. It's a really old book, dated 1545, when Michelangelo was still alive. I'll go and get it.

Nonno climbs up the ladder leaning against the bookshelf. He stretches over to one side to get the book, but - oh no! - it slips out of his hand. Ann, is sitting on the floor looking at the photographs in another volume when the book crashes down on her head, like this:

And a terrible thing happens: Ann is on the floor, completely covered by the book, and then ...she ... disappears ... Nonno comes down the ladder, picks up the book and examines it, but he is totally baffled ....

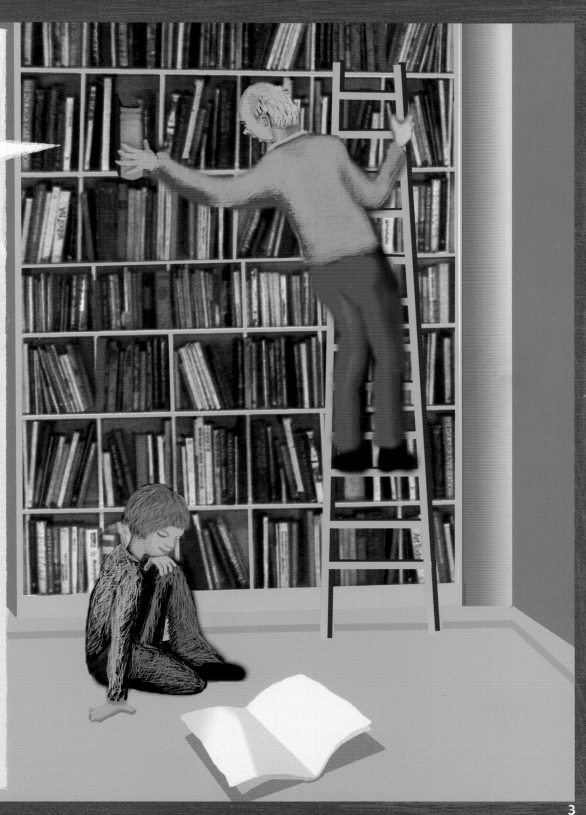

Ann suddenly finds herself in the year 1545, the same year as the book. And, would you believe it, she is in Michelangelo's house in the centre of Rome. After a moment of bewilderment Ann, who is an inquisitive girl, stands up and goes into the first room along the corridor. There is a boy preparing colours. In those days they didn't have tubes of paint like we have nowadays. To make a colour you had to crumble mineral stones and grind them with a pestle for hours on end. The boy's name is Lucio, and he is an apprentice of Michelangelo's, and he is obviously very surprised to see Ann.

Lucio, who is of a kind and helpful nature, thinks that Ann has come from far away to meet Michelangelo, and he finds a way to please her.

If you like I can introduce him to you. You can even stay here a few days and help me but I have to find an excuse. I can say that you're my cousin who has come a long way to visit me. But you have to pretend to be a boy because girls don't become painters.

My name's Ann and I come from America but I've been living in Rome for about a year now.

I was looking at a book on Michelangelo when something strange happened and now I'm here and I don't know where I am.

Hey who are you and where do you come from?

What ? I've heard that only barbarians live there and I don't believe you anyway. Nobody would come from America to live here. Well tell me what do you want ?

Michelangelo? But he's my Master!

In Michelangelo's studio Ann and Lucio get down to work. They have to prepare a cartoon for the fresco that the maestro is painting in the Paolina Chapel in the Pope's palace.

Now I'll show you what you have to do. Take the needle and make holes along the lines of the cartoon. Be careful, it's a delicate job.

You sound like a real teacher; look, I used to do this at the nursery school!

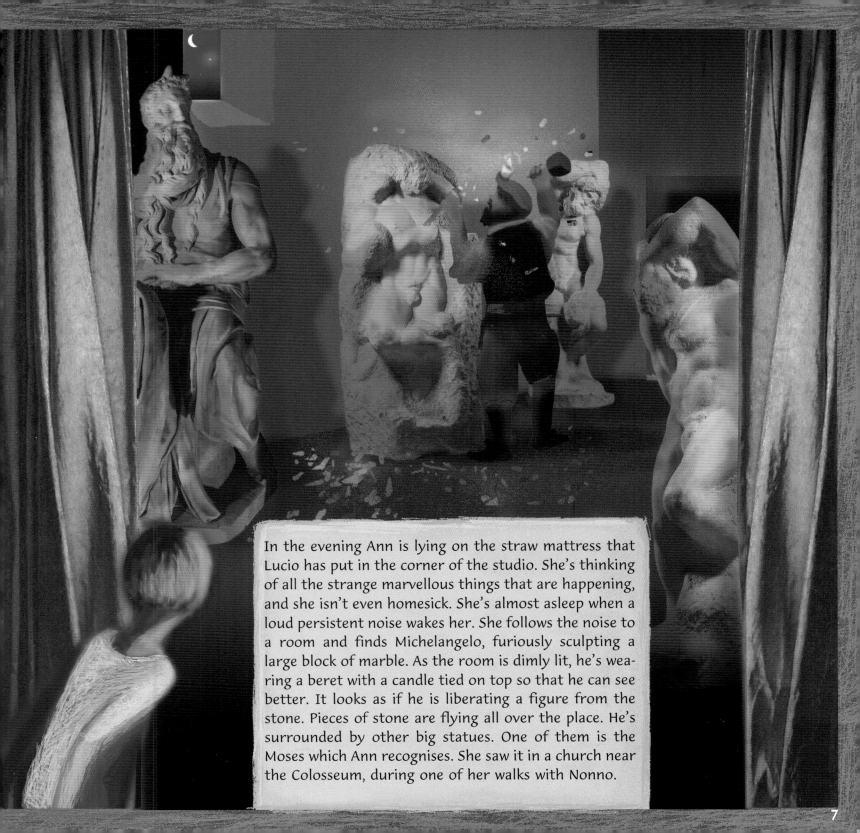

In the evening Ann is lying on the straw mattress that Lucio has put in the corner of the studio. She's thinking of all the strange marvellous things that are happening, and she isn't even homesick. She's almost asleep when a loud persistent noise wakes her. She follows the noise to a room and finds Michelangelo, furiously sculpting a large block of marble. As the room is dimly lit, he's wearing a beret with a candle tied on top so that he can see better. It looks as if he is liberating a figure from the stone. Pieces of stone are flying all over the place. He's surrounded by other big statues. One of them is the Moses which Ann recognises. She saw it in a church near the Colosseum, during one of her walks with Nonno.

Early the next morning they all go to the chapel.
Michelangelo is first, followed by Urbino, who has helped him for many years, then Lucio and last of all Ann, who is flabbergasted by what she sees.

Rome is so different that she doesn't recognise it. The first thing she notices is that there are no cars, just people on foot and a few carts drawn by a horse or a mule. Instead of shops there are stalls along the streets. Rich people can afford colourful clothes, but the many beggars wear grey rags. And there is such a stench, as the muddy streets are full of horse manure.

How nice! Horses instead of cars!

The Pope's palace is enormous. To get to the Paolina chapel you have to go through long corridors, rooms full of statues and beautiful paintings, courtyards and gardens. The chapel is in a mess because Michelangelo is painting the stories of the Apostles Peter and Paul. Lucio and Ann help him to get everything ready for the day's work. Ann pours colours into the bowls. Urbino has already spread the lime on the part of the wall that has to be painted today, and then he beats with a bag full of coal dust on the punctured lines of the cartoon which Ann and Lucio hold against the wall. Before starting, Michelangelo sends them all away. When he paints he always wants to be left alone.

Lucio wants to show Ann the wall of the Sistine Chapel, where Michelangelo had finished the huge fresco of the Last Judgement a few years earlier.
He had already painted the vault of the chapel in 1512, long before Lucio was born.

Look at it ! A fresco with more than 300 figures. Only my master knows how to paint something like that.

Look Lucio, I've already been in this place. When I came I had to queue for two hours and I wasn't allowed to speak inside the Chapel. But it's beautiful seeing it without any tourists!

What are you talking about, you're mad. You are only allowed in here when the Pope celebrates the Mass or by special request. Painters come every now and then to paint the figures of the fresco. You're saying a lot of strange things. Do you feel all right?

You see, here they are rebuilding St. Peter's. It will become the biggest church in the world, except that the architects don't get on with the work. Nobody knows what will happen.

I'll tell you what'll happen: St. Peter's will be grandiose and wonderful and Michelangelo will build the dome. I went up it once. You can see the whole of Rome from up there.

What dome are you talking about? Maybe you've got the wrong place; there is a beautiful dome in Florence. Can you tell the future?

Lucio is very proud of his Maestro's works and wants to show Ann everything. They go out of the Papal palace to have a look at Saint Peter's. The old basilica has already been partially demolished to make room for the new church.

After admiring the Pietà, Lucio and Ann go back into the Papal palace. They wander around until they find themselves behind a curtain, and overhear Architect Antonio da Sangallo talking to a cardinal about his plans for the rebuilding of St. Peter's Basilica.

It looks interesting.

I've never really liked the frescoes in the Sistine chapel anyway.

Well your Eminence, a part of the Sistine chapel and the Paolina chapel need to be demolished in order to carry out this project to build the most beautiful church in the world. As you can see from this model it's the only way to build a really special church.

They're crazy ! I'd better warn Michelangelo. They want to ruin his work.

Yes let's go !

Michelangelo gets angry when Lucio and Ann interrupt him while he's painting. But when he hears about Sangallo's plans he furiously jumps down off the scaffolding and they all go together to see the Pope.

Your Holiness, Sangallo wants to demolish the Sistine chapel and even the one I'm painting now!

Michelangelo, you always exaggerate; why would Sangallo plan such a thing whe he himself built my Paolina chapel?

Because he wants to ruin my work!

All right, I'll find out about that and if what you say is true then I'll stop the work on St. Peter's. In the meantime start thinking about the dome; you'll see, in the end you'll be the one to do it.

Didn't I tell you that Michelangelo would build the dome?. Isn't the Pope's dog nice?

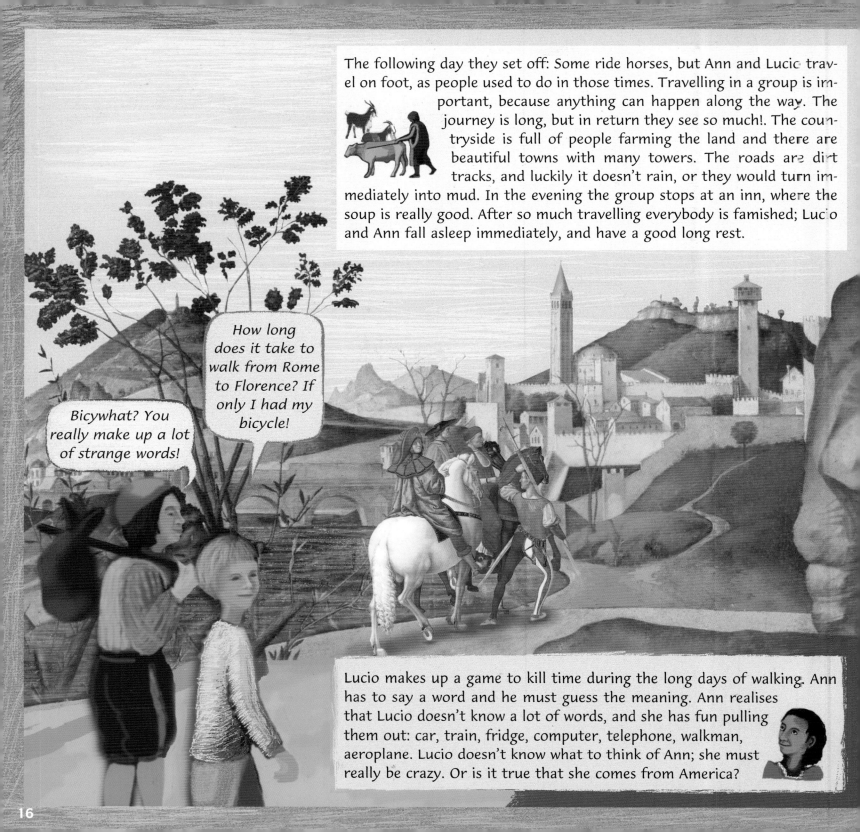

The following day they set off: Some ride horses, but Ann and Lucio travel on foot, as people used to do in those times. Travelling in a group is important, because anything can happen along the way. The journey is long, but in return they see so much!. The countryside is full of people farming the land and there are beautiful towns with many towers. The roads are dirt tracks, and luckily it doesn't rain, or they would turn immediately into mud. In the evening the group stops at an inn, where the soup is really good. After so much travelling everybody is famished; Lucio and Ann fall asleep immediately, and have a good long rest.

How long does it take to walk from Rome to Florence? If only I had my bicycle!

Bicywhat? You really make up a lot of strange words!

Lucio makes up a game to kill time during the long days of walking. Ann has to say a word and he must guess the meaning. Ann realises that Lucio doesn't know a lot of words, and she has fun pulling them out: car, train, fridge, computer, telephone, walkman, aeroplane. Lucio doesn't know what to think of Ann; she must really be crazy. Or is it true that she comes from America?

Lucio, wait, this statue is very famous! It's the David!

Of course it's famous. Michelangelo made it. But come on, we have to enter here!

At last they are in Florence. What a magnificent city, so different from Rome! So many grand palaces, and clean streets! They stop in front of Palazzo della Signoria. It's where they must ask for Michelangelo's drawings. In the square there is a wonderful statue, the David, sculpted by Michelangelo and dedicated to his city. Lucio told Ann that Michelangelo found a block of marble in the garden of the Duomo. Many years beforehand another sculptor had started to work on it and had ruined it. The block had been abandoned there for years, because it was of no use to anybody. So it was a surprise to everyone that such a statue could be carved from that faulty block.

A very distinct gentleman shows them the panorama of the city and the Duomo from the roof of the Palazzo. While Ann runs around looking at the view, Lucio gets the drawings of the dome built by Brunelleschi.

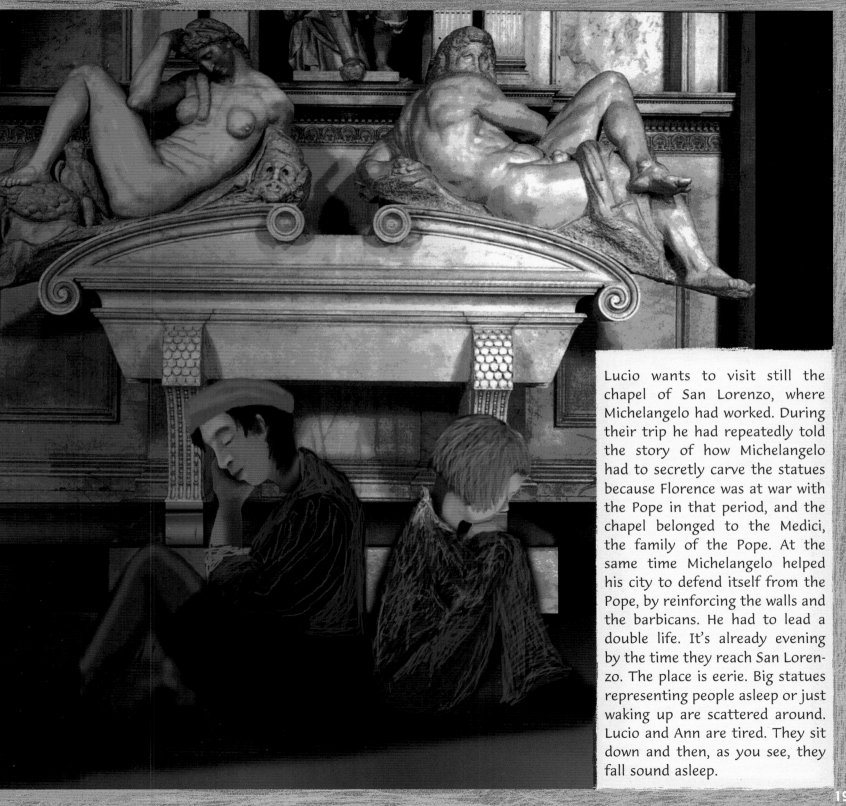

Lucio wants to visit still the chapel of San Lorenzo, where Michelangelo had worked. During their trip he had repeatedly told the story of how Michelangelo had to secretly carve the statues because Florence was at war with the Pope in that period, and the chapel belonged to the Medici, the family of the Pope. At the same time Michelangelo helped his city to defend itself from the Pope, by reinforcing the walls and the barbicans. He had to lead a double life. It's already evening by the time they reach San Lorenzo. The place is eerie. Big statues representing people asleep or just waking up are scattered around. Lucio and Ann are tired. They sit down and then, as you see, they fall sound asleep.

The long return journey to Rome is over.
From a hill they look at the city lying at their feet. Ann can't believe her eyes. Is that it? Rome is small, and she had never noticed all those towers! How many boats there are on the Tiber river!

I was born here, but I had never seen the city from here. How beautiful Rome is!

The only thing I recognise is the Pantheon, that big dome, but where is the rest?

Look, the Capitol was once the most important hill in Rome, and the ancient Romans had it covered with temples. I imagine a place like this as a scenario for many events, like a balcony on the city with a monumental staircase... But, are you listening to me?

The following day Michelangelo is so happy to receive the drawings from Lucio and Ann that he brings them around Rome. From a terrace of a palace there is a nice view of the Capitol Hill. Michelangelo has the task of rebuilding the square and the Palaces of the Town Hall. First of all, he placed the equestrian statue of Marcus Aurelius in the centre, and has already got grandiose ideas of how to arrange the rest.

I live nearby.

Then, shouldn't you go back home?

Later on Michelangelo calls the boys in his studio. Even though he doesn't show it, he isn't very convinced about that cousin of Lucio's. And there is another thing. He has found a very old book, but the date says it has just been printed, therefore it should be new.

I found this book in the corridor; it doesn't belong to me but I saw my name in it; Gianni, do you know anything about it?

Yes, the book belongs to Nonno, I would like to bring it back to him.

PROFILO DELLA CVPOLA DI S. MARIA DEL FIORE DI FIRENZA

Ann is happy she has found the book Nonno had taken off the shelf the day her adventure began. It must be a magic book. It is nice to live for a while in a different time, but now she only wanted to sleep in her own bed.

Ann explains to Lucio that the book is magic, and that he has to drop it on her head so that she can go back home. Lucio starts laughing but then decides to help her. He drops the book from the window, and the book doesn't fall, but floats down like a feather, getting bigger and bigger ... When the book touches Ann's head, it envelops her completely ... and they both disappear. Lucio is bewildered! His friend Ann has disappeared into thin air, just as he was getting to like her! But it's true that he had always thought that she was bewitched!

Ann is lying on the ground in front of Nonno's bookshelves. He has been so worried about her disappearance that he consulted several books on the subject of "old magic books". He hasn't found a solution to the mystery and is about to go to the police, when, all of a sudden, he hears the thud of a falling book and there is Ann, alive and well, and fast asleep. Nonno wakes her up and Ann is so happy to see him that she throws her arms around him and says: "Nonno, did you know that Michelangelo has an apprentice called Lucio?" Nonno, used to always knowing everything, thinks about it for a minute and says: "No, I must confess I have never read anything about this Lucio, you must have dreamt it..."